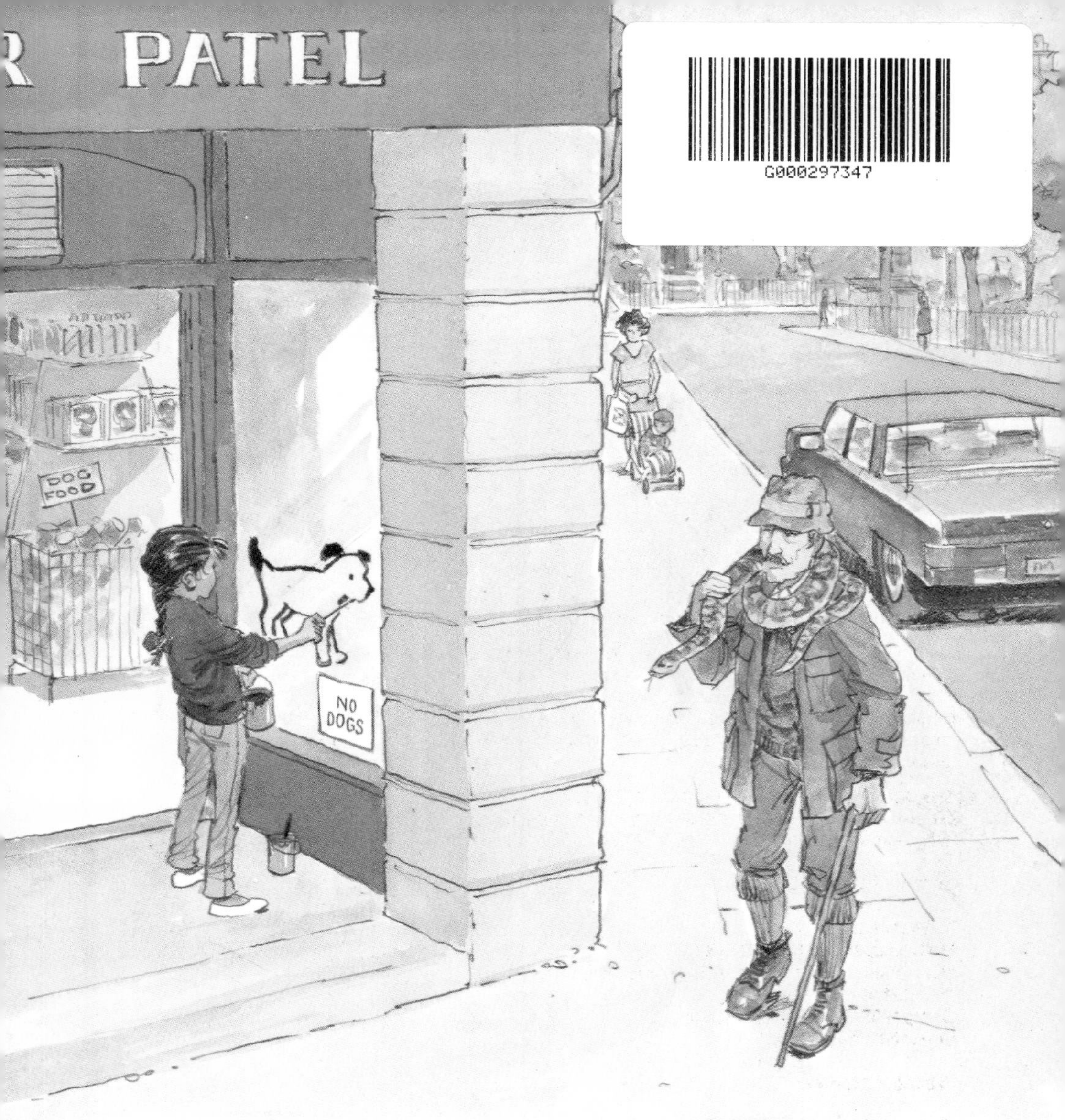
PATEL
DOG FOOD
NO DOGS

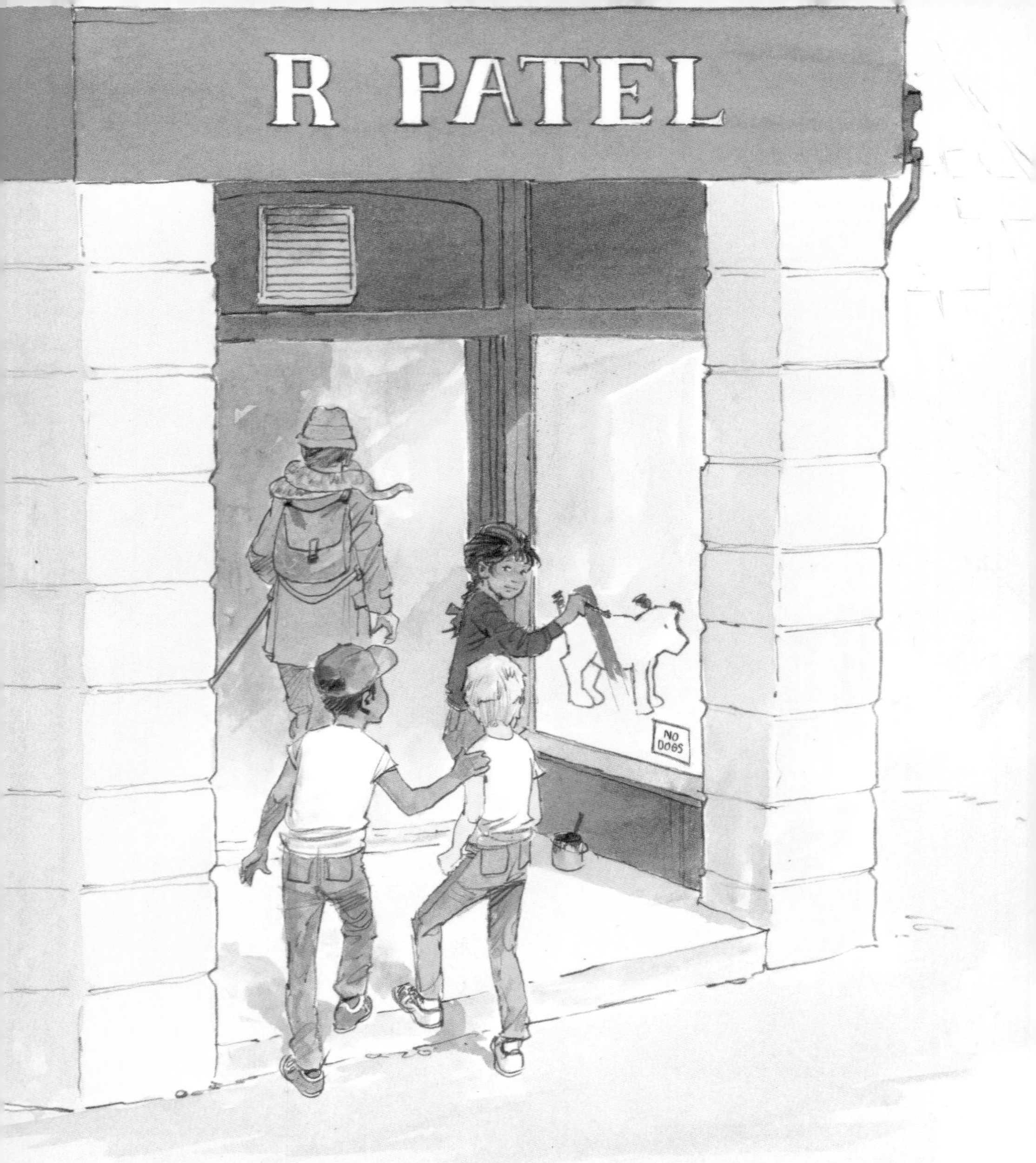
R PATEL
NO DOGS

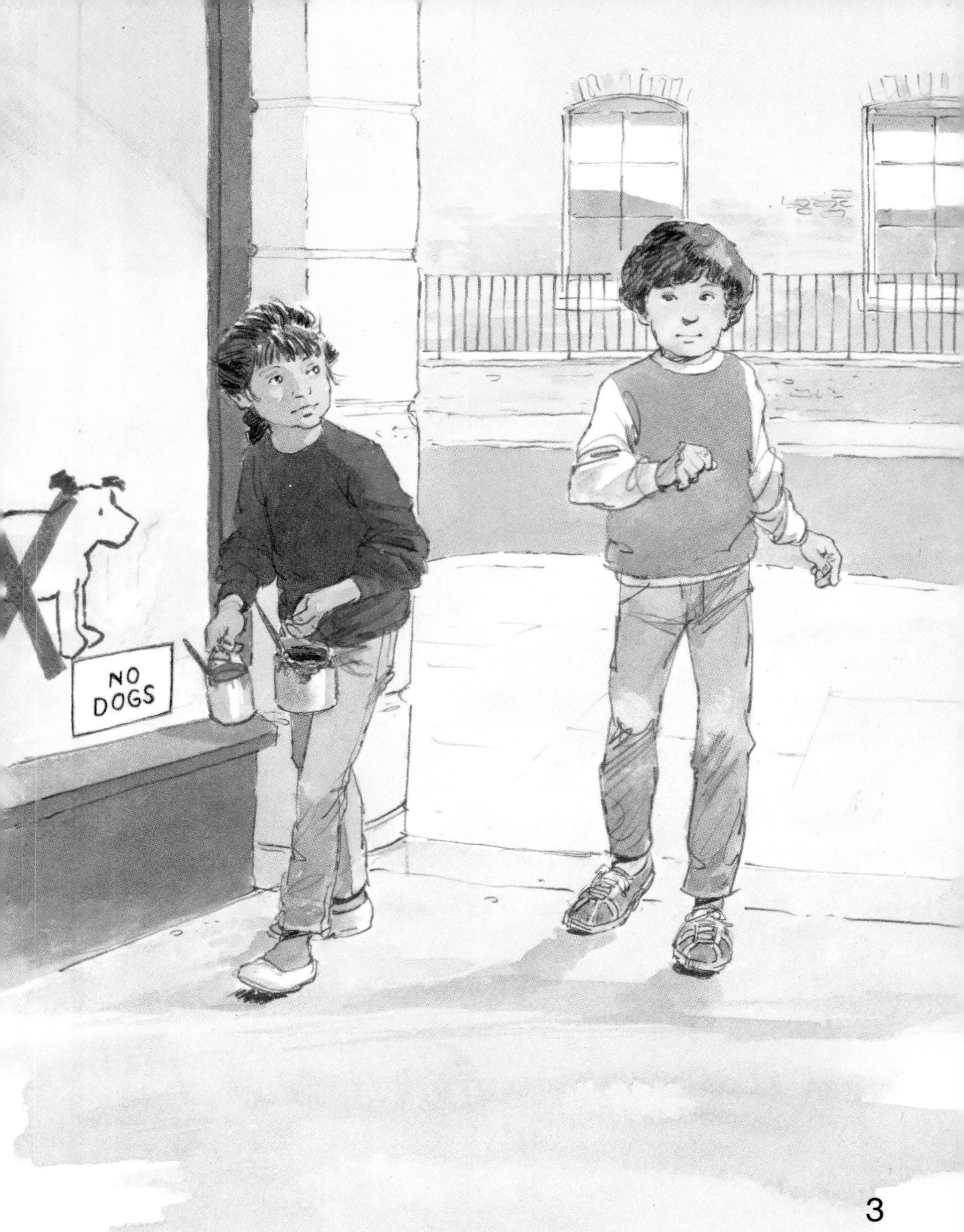
NO
DOGS

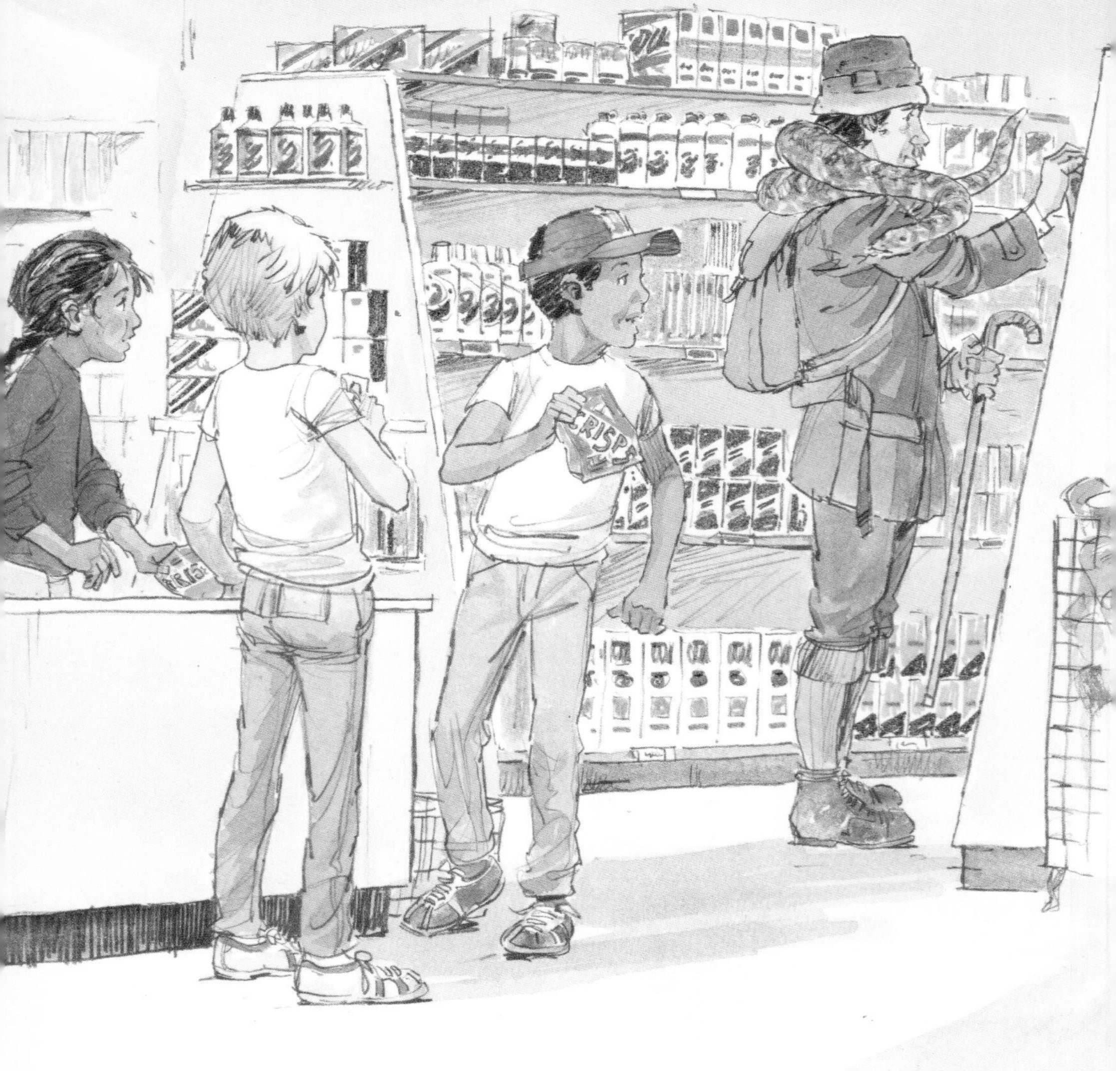

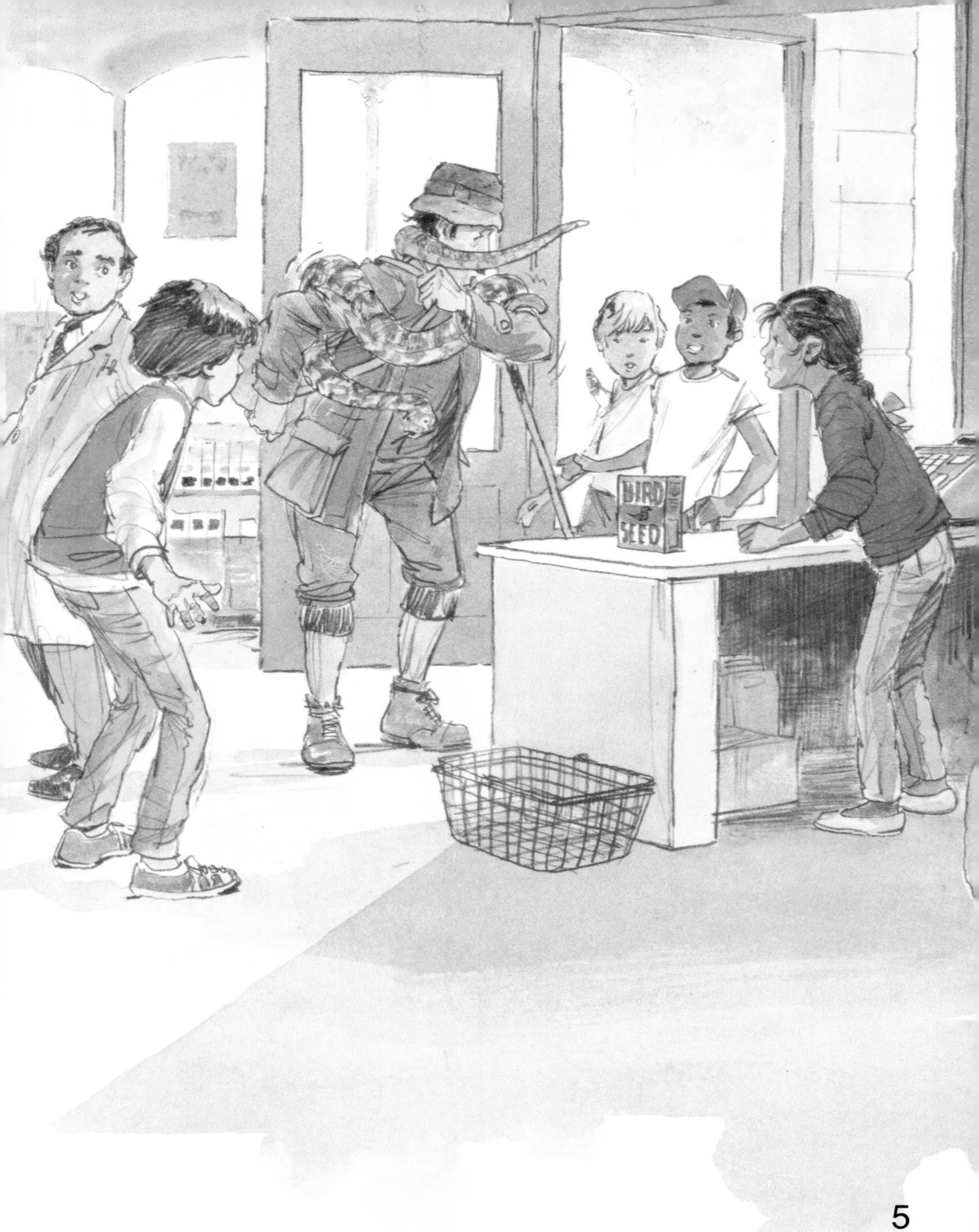
BIRD
SEED

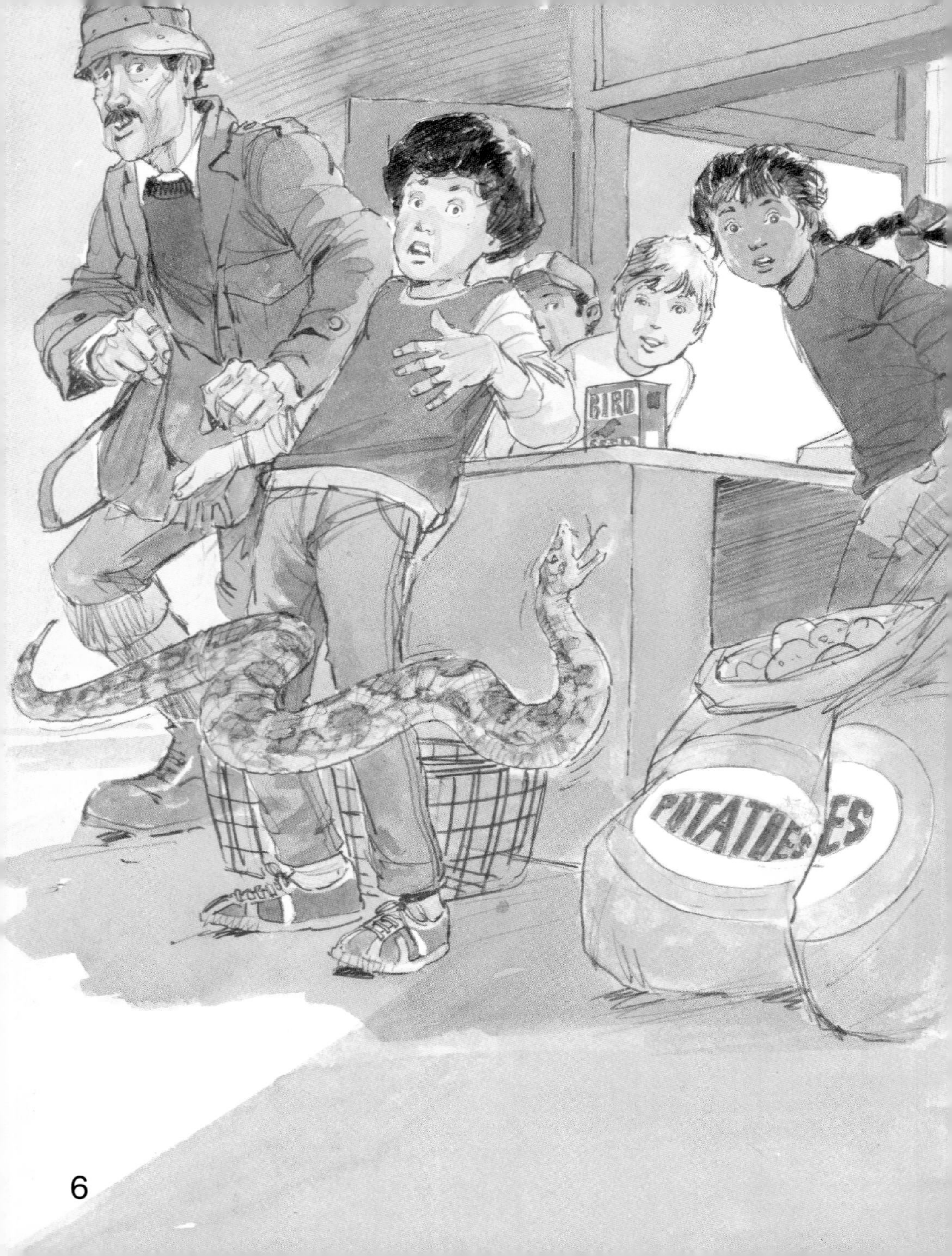
BIRD
POTATOES

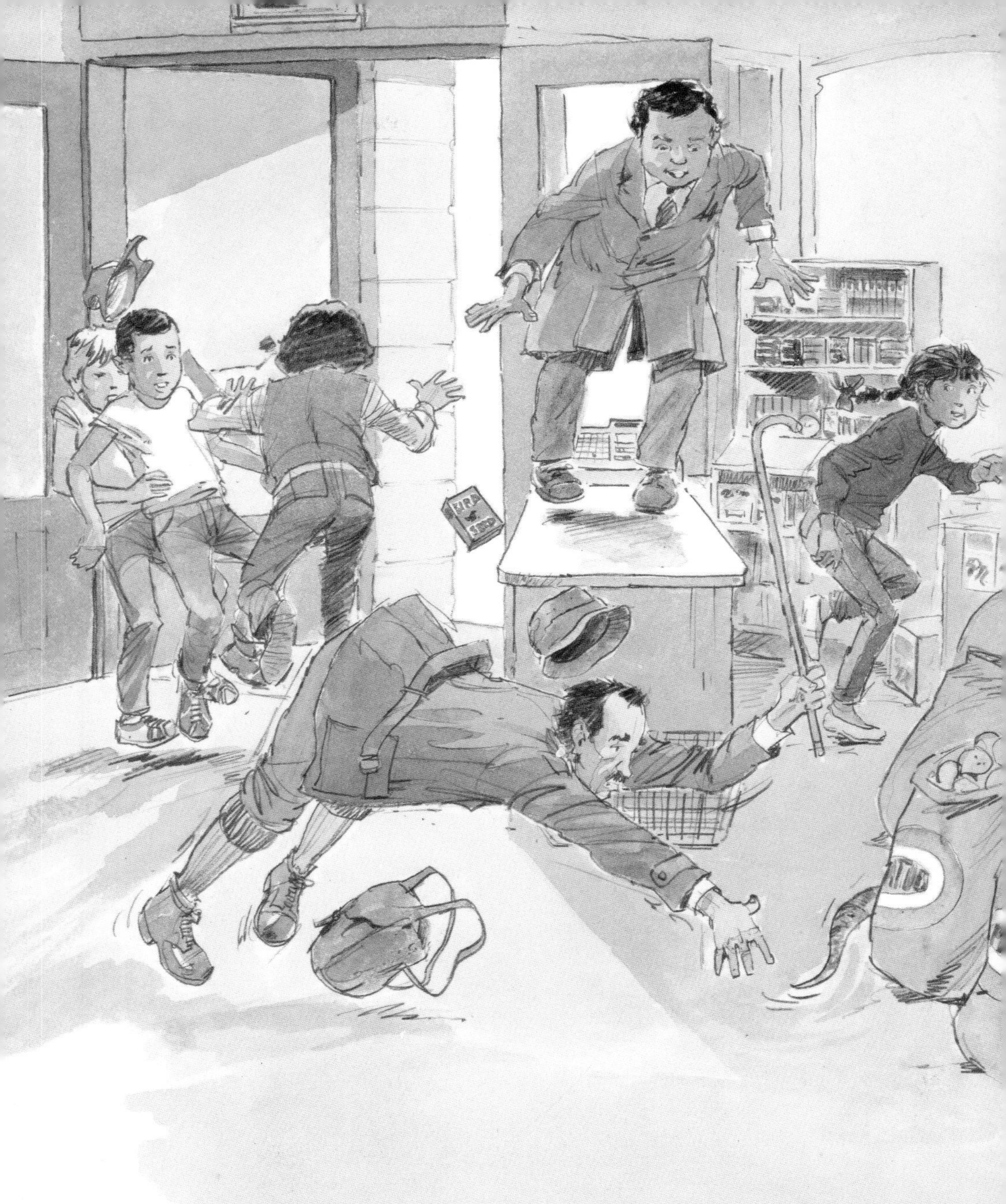

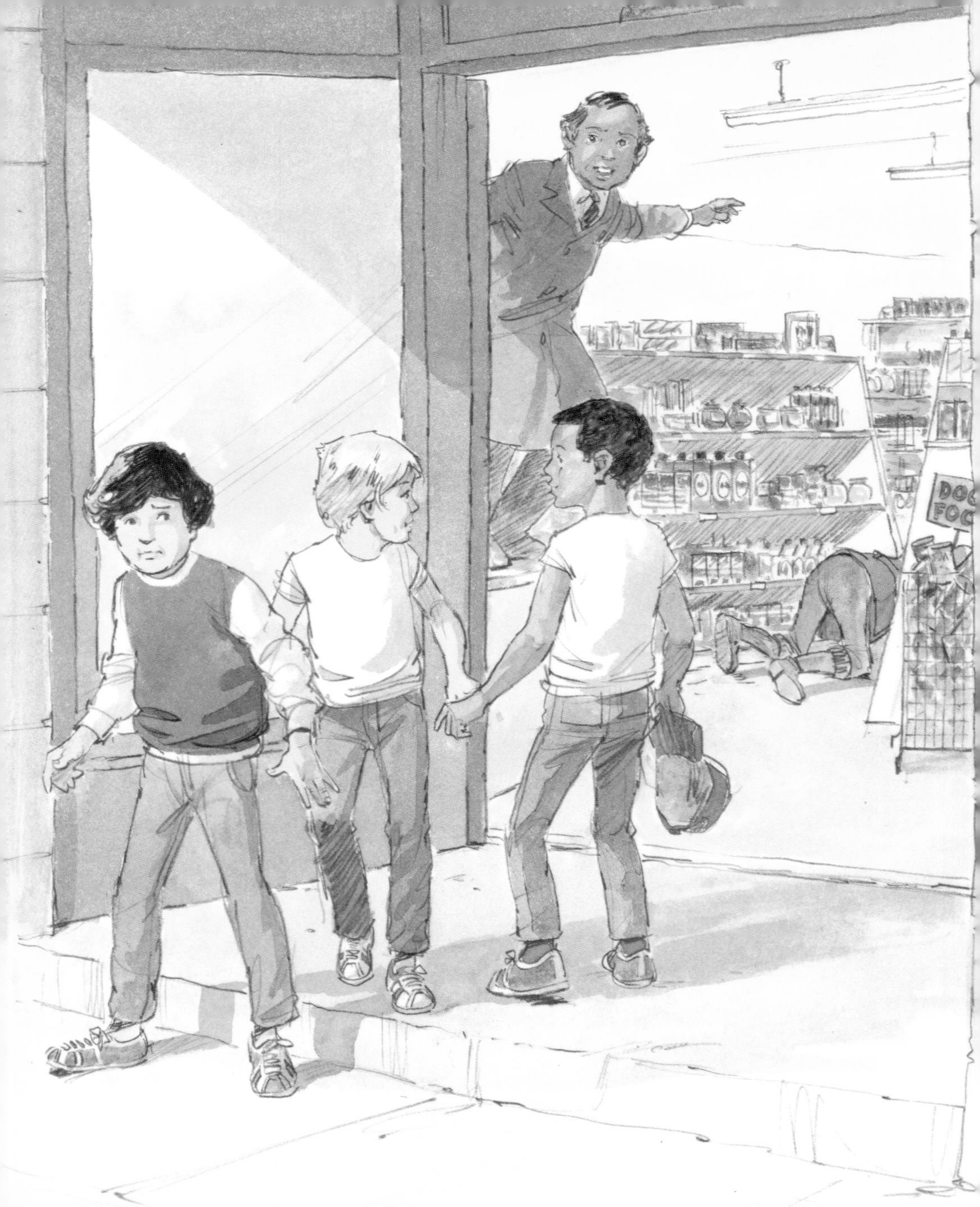

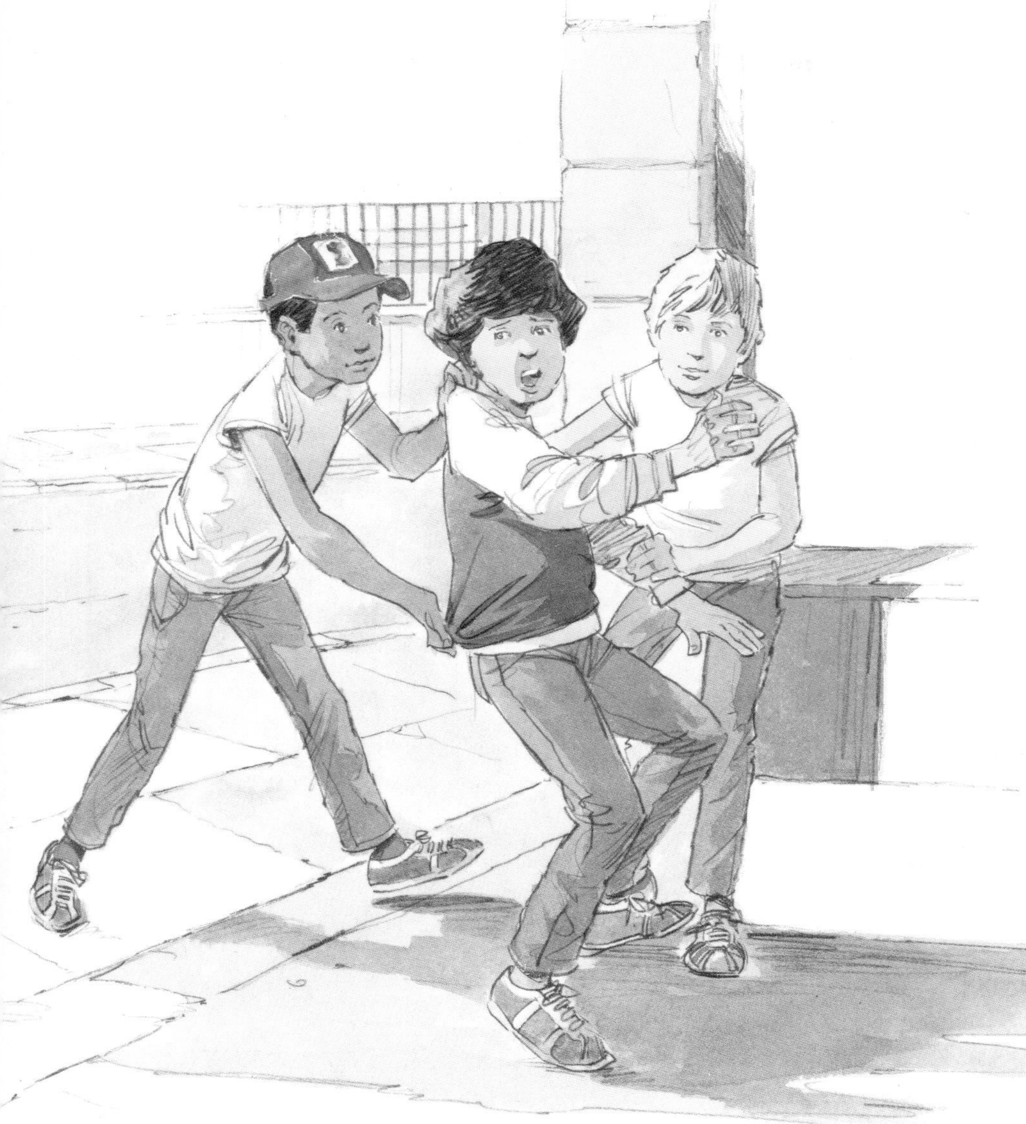

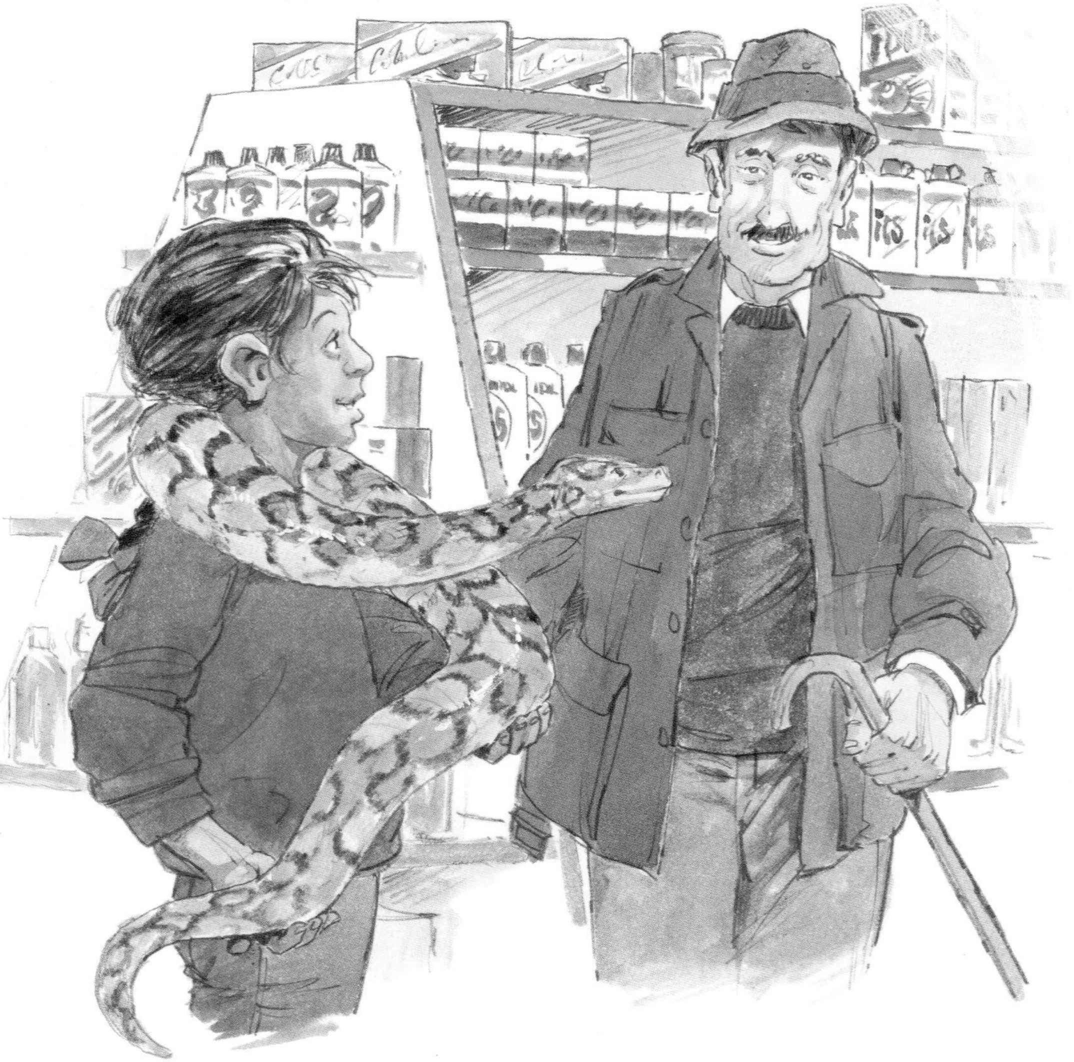

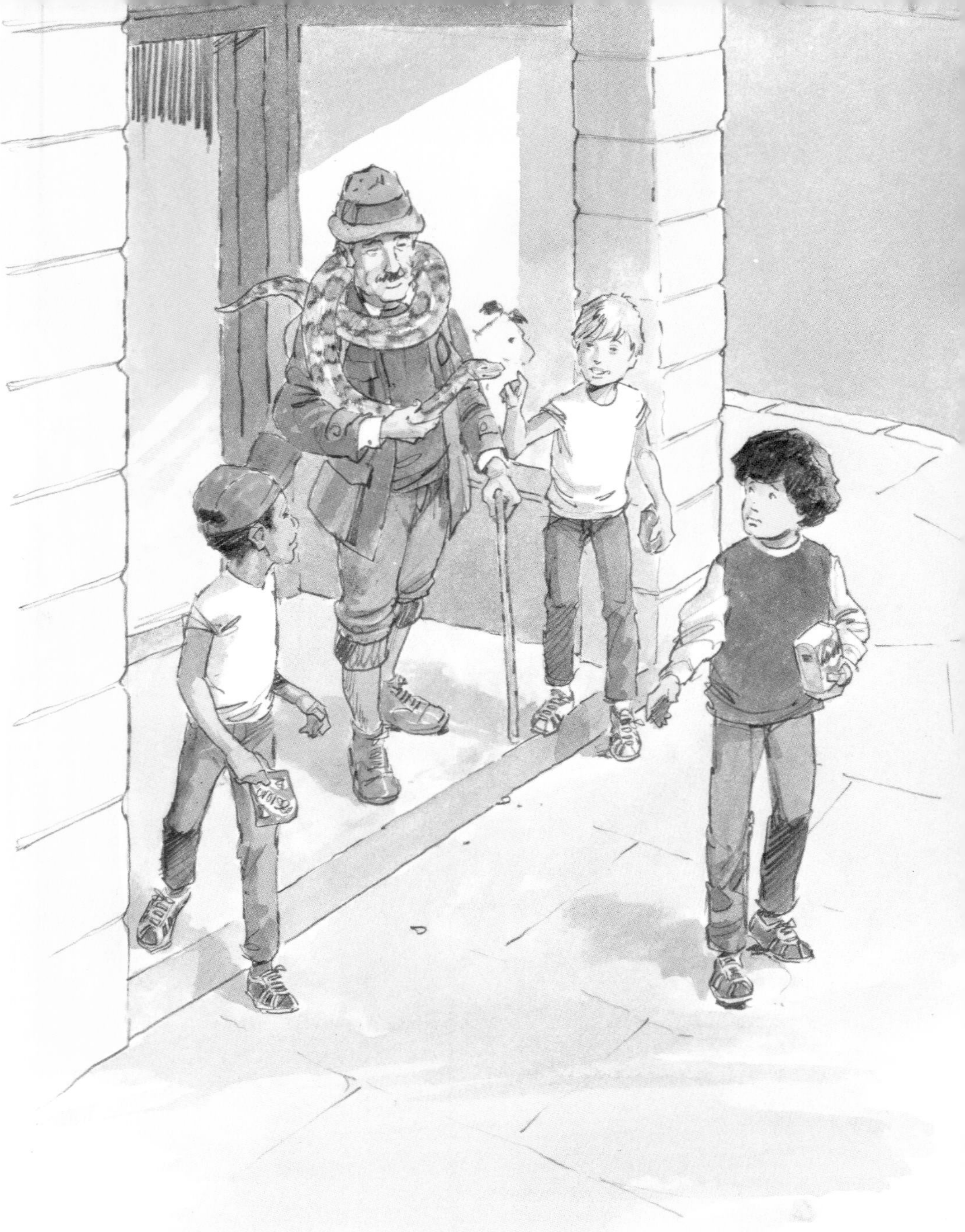

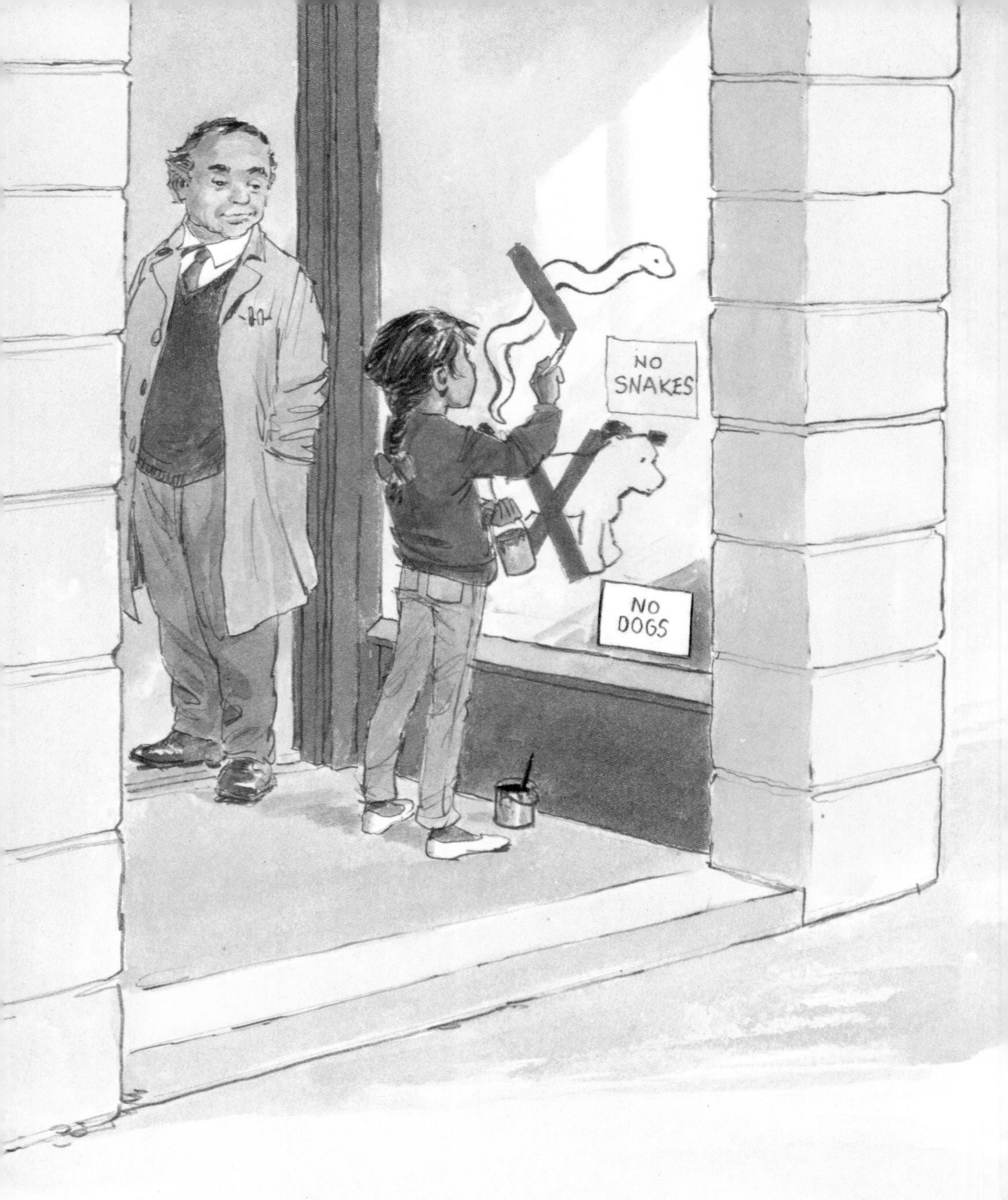
NO SNAKES
NO DOGS